RISING ★ STARS

ASSESSMENT

Science
Progress Tests

Year

2

Pauline Hannigan
Series Advisors: Cornwall Learning

Rising Stars UK Ltd, 7 Hatchers Mews, Bermondsey Street, London SE1 3GS

www.risingstars-uk.com

First published 2014

All facts are correct at time of going to press. All referenced websites were correct at the time this book went to press.

Author: Pauline Hannigan
Educational consultant: Ed Walsh, Cornwall Learning
Accessibility reviewer: Vivien Kilburn
Editorial: Susan Gardner, David Mantovani and Lynette Woodward
Typist: Rosalyn Dale
Design: Ray Rich and Clive Sutherland
Illustrations: Oxford Designers and Illustrators
Photos: istockphoto.com
Cover design: Burville-Riley Partnership

Rising Stars is grateful to the following people and schools who contributed to the development of these materials.
Plumcroft Primary School, London; Rainford Brook Lodge Primary School, Merseyside; St Nicholas CE Primary School, Chislehurst; St Margaret's CE Primary School, Heywood, Rochdale; Tennyson Road Primary School, Luton

British Library Cataloguing in Publication Data.
A CIP record for this book is available from the British Library.
ISBN: 978 1 84680 961 3

MIX
Paper from responsible sources
FSC® C011748

Printed by Ashford Colour Press

Contents

Introduction

Why use Rising Stars Assessment Progress Tests?

The *Rising Stars Assessment Science Progress Tests* have been developed to support teachers assess the progress their pupils are making against the 2014 National Curriculum Programme of Study for science. The tests are designed to support effective classroom assessment across Years 1 to 6 and are easy to use and mark.

The tests are organised around the topics in the Programme of Study and have been:
- written by primary science assessment specialists
- reviewed by primary science curriculum and assessment experts.

How do the tests track progress?

The results data from the tests can be used to track progress. They show whether pupils are making the expected progress for their year, more than expected progress or less than expected progress. This data can then be used alongside other evidence to enable effective planning of future teaching and learning, for reporting to parents and as evidence for Ofsted inspections. If teachers are using the CD-ROM version of the tests, the results data can be keyed into the Progress Tracker (see page 7 for more information), which automatically shows the progress of individual pupils against the Programme of Study and the results for all pupils by question and test. Data can also be exported into the school's management information system (MIS).

About the Science Progress Tests

The tests are written to match the content requirements of the Programme of Study for the 2014 National Curriculum. The content areas are:

Content	Year 1	Year 2	Year 3	Year 4	Year 5	Year 6
Living things (and their habitats)		✓		✓	✓	✓
Plants	✓	✓	✓			
Animals, including humans	✓	✓	✓	✓	✓	✓
Evolution and inheritance						✓
Materials (uses, properties and changes)	✓	✓			✓	
Rocks			✓			
States of matter				✓		
Light			✓			✓
Sound				✓		
Seasonal changes/Earth and space	✓				✓	
Forces (and magnets)			✓		✓	
Electricity				✓		✓

In line with the Programme of Study, the skills of working scientifically are assessed through all the content areas rather than separately. For each content area there are four tests:
- Test 1(diagnostic) – note that for Years 1 and 2 this is a checklist rather than a test to make it more accessible and informative for pupils whose written language skills are likely to be less developed

- Test 2(mid-topic)
- Test 3(end of topic)
- Test 4(end of year)

The marks for each test are as follows:

Test	Number of marks					
	Year 1	Year 2	Year 3	Year 4	Year 5	Year 6
Test/Checklist 1 (diagnostic)	N/A	N/A	10	10	10	10
Test 2 (mid-topic)	10	10	10	10	10	10
Test 3 (end of topic)	10	10	10	10	10	10
Test 4 (end of year)	10	10	10	10	10	10

Test demand

The first test for each topic is designed to help teachers assess the prior learning of individual pupils and the class before teaching begins. These tests/checklists are more open-ended than tests 2–4 to elicit as much information as possible to help teachers refine their plans for teaching the topic.

Test 2 is designed to be used during a topic, test 3 at the end of a topic and test 4 at the end of the year. Test 4 could optionally be used as an alternative or additional test at the end of a topic. Tests 2–4 follow the same approach. In each test:

- 5 marks are allocated to knowledge and understanding
- 5 marks are allocated to application
- 4 marks additionally assess working scientifically.

Tests 2–4 also contain a mix of objective questions and questions requiring written answers.

Tracking progress

The marks pupils score in the tests can be used to track how they are progressing against the expected outcomes for their year group in relation to the National Curriculum Programme of Study. The marks for tests 2–4 for each topic have been split into three progress zones:

- less than expected progress
- expected progress
- more than expected progress.

The zones for each year group are as follows:

	Test	Zone mark range		
		Less than expected progress	Expected progress	More than expected progress
Year 1	2–4	0–5	6–8	9–10
Year 2	2–4	0–5	6–8	9–10
Year 3	2–4	0–5	6–8	9–10
Year 4	2–4	0–5	6–8	9–10
Year 5	2–4	0–5	6–8	9–10
Year 6	2–4	0–5	6–8	9–10

The table gives the mark ranges for the progress zones for each test which you can use to see how well each pupil is doing in each test. If pupils are making the expected progress for their year they will be consistently scoring marks in the middle zone of marks in the tests. The higher the mark in the zone, the more secure you can be that they are making expected progress.

Determining prior learning

The first test for each topic is provided to help teachers find out about prior learning.

For Years 1 and 2 these tests are in the form of diagnostic checklists to enable an oral investigation of prior learning as it is recognised that pupils have limited reading and writing vocabularies, particularly in Year 1. Each checklist comprises a set of questions to ask pupils and supporting visual prompts. There is also a Pupil Responses Form that can be used to record whether some, most or all pupils are able to answer each question.

For Years 3–6 there is a diagnostic test for each topic. These tests can be administered as described below and the marks analysed to identify the prior learning of individual pupils and the class as a whole.

How to use the Science Progress Tests

Preparation and timings

1 Make enough copies of the test(s) for each pupil to have their own copy.
2 Hand out the papers and ensure pupils are seated appropriately so that they can't see each other's papers.
3 Pupils will need pens or pencils, rulers and erasers. Encourage pupils to cross out answers rather than rub them out.
4 There are no time limits for the tests but normal practice is to allow a minute per mark for written tests. Help with reading may be given using the same rules as when providing a reader with the DfE KS2 tests.

Supporting pupils during the tests

Before the test explain to the pupils that the test is an opportunity to show what they know, understand and can do. They should try to answer all the questions but should not worry if there are some they can't do.

Many pupils will be able to work independently in the tests, with minimal support from the teacher or a teaching assistant. However, pupils should be encouraged to 'have a go' at a question, or to move on to a fresh question if they appear to be stuck, to ensure that no pupil becomes distressed.

It is important that pupils receive appropriate support, but are not unfairly advantaged or disadvantaged. Throughout the tests, therefore, the teacher may read, explain or sign to a pupil any parts of the test that include instructions, for example by demonstrating how to circle an answer.

With younger age groups you may also consider using the version of the test on the CD-ROM and projecting it on to a whiteboard to support a whole class or group to take the tests. You may choose to refer to the words on the whiteboard and read them aloud so that pupils can follow them on the screen and on their own test paper and then write their answers on their papers individually.

Marking the tests

Use the detailed mark scheme and your professional judgement to award marks. **Do not award half marks.**

It is useful to use peer marking of test questions from time to time. Pupils should exchange test sheets and mark them as you read out the question and answer. You will need to check that pupils are marking accurately. This approach also provides an opportunity to recap on any questions that pupils found difficult to answer.

Feeding back to pupils

Once the test has been marked, use a five-minute feedback session with the pupils to help them review their answers. Wherever possible pupils should be encouraged to make their own corrections as in this way they will become more aware of their own strengths and weaknesses. Agree with each pupil what they did well in the test and what the targets are for them to improve. A template 'My Progress' sheet is provided on page 8 for this purpose. Encourage pupils to colour the face that best shows how well they think they did in the test (there are three faces to choose from – one happy, one sad, and one neutral). They should then add the number of the question that they found most difficult. Finally, pupils should fill in the speech bubble to indicate what they need more help with. Some pupils will be able to do this themselves but some may find a word bank supplied by the teacher useful. The teacher or another adult may need to act as scribe for some pupils.

Using the Progress Tracker

The second table on page 5 gives the mark ranges for the progress zones for each test, which you can use to see how well each pupil is doing in each test and across each topic. If pupils are making the expected progress for their year they will be consistently scoring marks in the middle zone of marks in the tests. The higher the mark in the zone, the more secure you can be that they are making expected progress.

The CD-ROM* version of *Science Progress Tests* includes an interactive Progress Tracker, which allows you to enter the marks for each question for each test by pupil. This then automatically shows you which zone the pupil is in and also the zone distribution for the class so that you can track the progress of individual pupils and the whole class.

The Progress Tracker also enables you to review the marks for each question so that you can identify areas where some or all pupils may need further support and areas where some or all pupils are ready to be stretched further. It also provides a separate summary of marks for each pupil for knowledge and understanding, application, and working scientifically so that you can identify if pupils have strengths or weaknesses in a particular area.

If required, data from the tests can be exported into the school's management information system (MIS) so that it can be used alongside other data in whole school monitoring including the monitoring of specific groups of pupils, such as Pupil Premium.

Full details about the Progress Tracker are provided on the CD-ROM.

* If you have the book version only of *Science Progress Tests*, the Progress Tracker can be downloaded from bit.ly/progtracker

My progress

Name: _____ Class: _____ Date: _____

Test: _____

★ How well did you do?

★ Which question did you find the hardest?

★ What do you need more help with?

Year 2
Living things and their habitats
Test 1 (diagnostic assessment)

	Question	Answer	Extra information
1.	Can you tell me the name of something that is alive?	Specific name of any plant or animal or group of plants or animals (e.g. tree, human)	
2.	Can you tell me the name of something that has never been alive?	Any inanimate object, e.g. cup, stone	A named wooden object (e.g. pencil) will need further questioning to determine understanding of where wood comes from.
3.	Where might a fish live?	Sea, river, stream, pond	Fish tank or aquarium are acceptable.
4.	Can you name any of these animals? How can you find out if you do not know?	Spider, fly, woodlouse, ant Research, e.g. Internet, books	*Use the pictures on page 10.* The second question gives an indication of the pupils' awareness of how to access information.
5.	Can you tell me the name of an animal that eats grass?	Any grass-eating herbivore (domestic or wild), e.g. cow, sheep, horse, goat, rabbit, deer	
6.	Can you tell me the name of an animal that people sometimes eat?	Any commonly eaten animal, e.g. cow, chicken, sheep, pig, fish	Named meats (e.g. pork, beef); will need further questioning to determine that they come from animals.

Living things and their habitats
Test 1 (diagnostic assessment): pupil responses form

Q	Some pupils	Most pupils	All pupils
1.			
2.			
3.			
4.			
5.			
6.			

Year 2
Living things and their habitats
Test 1 (diagnostic assessment): question 4, visual prompts

Year 2
Living things and their habitats Test 2 (mid-topic)

Name: _____ Class: _____ Date: _____

1. **a)** Sort these things into two groups. Draw arrows.

dog

laptop

tree

baby

car

log

A

B

living thing or things that have been alive

non-living things

KU/WS

2 marks

b) Write one more thing that could go in group A.

....

A

1 mark

c) Write one more thing that could go in group B.

....

A

1 mark

Total for this page

2. What do all animals do that makes them alive?
    Write **three** things.

    i) ....

    ii) ....

    iii) ....

KU

3 marks

3. a) Class 2 go out into the school grounds to see what living
       things they can find.
       Complete the table, that shows what Class 2 found and
       where they found them.

		Name	Habitat
		daffodil	flower bed

A/WS

2 marks

    b) What is a 'habitat'?

    ....

    ....

A

1 mark

/10

Total for this test

Year 2
Living things and their habitats Test 3 (end of topic)

Name: _____ Class: _____ Date: _____

1. Daniel made this table to show where he found different animals.

In a flower bed	In a pond
5 caterpillars	1 frog
3 beetles	3 water-boatmen
2 worms	4 leeches

a) Where did Daniel find the leeches?

....

A/WS
☐
1 mark

b) What did he find most of in the flower bed?

....

A/WS
☐
1 mark

c) Why do caterpillars like living in flower beds?

....

....

KU
☐
1 mark

d) Write **one** reason why caterpillars don't live in ponds.

....

....

KU
☐
1 mark

☐
Total for
this page

2. Class 2 were finding out about a rotting
log in the school garden.

a) Tick **two** animals they found under the log.

butterfly	slug	sparrow	woodlouse
☐	☐	☐	☐

KU
☐
2 marks

b) Write **one** reason why a log makes a good home for some
animals.

....

A
☐
1 mark

c) Class 2 recorded the number of animals they found on the
log.
Complete the table.

Animal	Tally	Number
worm	IIIII	5
snail	IIIII IIII	
slug		4
spider	III	
beetle		11

A/WS
☐
2 marks

3. **Carnivores** are animals that eat only meat.
Give the name of a carnivore.

KU
☐
1 mark

....

/10

**Total for
this test**

14

Year 2
Living things and their habitats Test 4 (end of year)

Name: _____ Class: _____ Date: _____

1. **Herbivores** are animals that eat only plants.
   Tick the animals that are herbivores.

   caterpillar ☐

   cow ☐

   snail ☐

   cat ☐

   man ☐

   KU ☐ 1 mark

2. **a)** Class 2 were finding out about what food different animals eat.

   i) Choose the correct animal to put in the box to finish the food chain.

   | man | snail | goat | owl |

   grass →(is eaten by)→ cow →(is eaten by)→ ☐

   grass   cow

   KU ☐ 1 mark

   ii) Choose **two** different animals to complete this food chain.

   leaf →(is eaten by)→ ☐ →(is eaten by)→ ☐

   KU ☐ 2 marks

   ☐ Total for this page

b) Class 2 wanted to find out what leaves snails like to eat best.

lettuce   cabbage   dandelion

Class 2 put four snails in a tank. What should they do next?
Tick **one**.

Give them a different leaf to eat every day ☐

Give them one of each leaf at the same time ☐

A/WS
☐
1 mark

c) Why should Class 2 do this?

A/WS
☐
1 mark

....

d) The next day Class 2 made this table to show what leaves
the snails had eaten:

Leaf	How much was eaten
lettuce	nearly all eaten
cabbage	half eaten
dandelion	only a little eaten

i) Which leaf do the snails seem to like best?

A/WS
☐
1 mark

....

ii) Which leaf do the snails seem not to like?

A/WS
☐
1 mark

....

e) Amy said they should do their test again the next day.
Is this a good idea?

yes ☐   **no** ☐

A
☐
1 mark

f) Why is it important that Class 2 put the snails back where
they found them when they had finished their test?

KU
☐
1 mark

....

/10

**Total for
this test**

Year 2
Plants

Test 1 (diagnostic assessment)

Question	Answer	Extra information
1. Can you tell me what grows from a seed?	A plant	Names of specific plants are acceptable.
2. What does a seed need to **start** growing?	Water (rain) and warmth	Note: seeds and bulbs need water to start to grow (germinate) and most need a rise in temperature; most do not need light as they have a store of food inside them (for initial growth) or soil.
3. Can you tell me the name of this and what it does?	A bulb that can grow into a plant	*Use a real bulb or picture (see page 18).* Names of specific plants (e.g. daffodil, bluebell) are acceptable.
4. Can you tell me how to look after this plant to keep it healthy?	Give it water and light; water it; put it in a warm place; put it by the window; put it in the sunshine	*Use a real, healthy plant or picture (see page 19).* Some pupils might refer to 'feeding' plants, as mineral supplements are often referred to as 'plant food' (not necessary for health).
5. Why might this plant be dying?	Any suitable reference to need for water, light or suitable temperature	*Use a real, unhealthy plant or picture (see page 20).* Reference to disease, damage, poison also acceptable.

Plants

Test 1 (diagnostic assessment): pupil responses form

Q	Some pupils	Most pupils	All pupils
1.			
2.			
3.			
4.			
5.			

Year 2
Plants Test 2 (mid-topic)

Name: _____ Class: _____ Date: _____

1. Class 2 have two plants in the classroom.

A

B

What may Class 2 have forgotten to do to Plant B?

_____

2. Class 2 have planted some daffodil bulbs in the garden outside the classroom.

a) How will they know when the bulbs have started to grow?

_____

b) Tick the season when this will happen.

winter ☐

summer ☐

spring ☐

autumn ☐

c) What will Class 2 see as the daffodils grow?

_____

3. Four children each grow ten plants.
They count how many of their plants grow well.
They make a bar chart of their results.

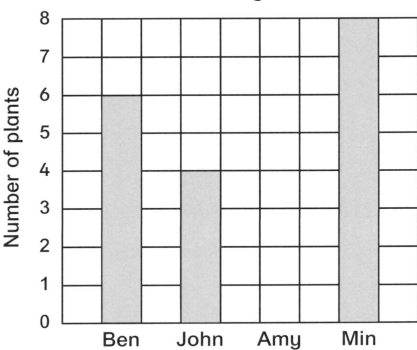

Plants that grow well

a) Five of Amy's plants grow well.
Draw her bar on the chart.

A/WS
☐
1 mark

b) Who grew the most plants well?

A/WS
☐
1 mark

....

c) Tick the **three** things that plants need to keep healthy.

light ☐

fresh air ☐

water ☐

to be outside ☐

soil ☐

KU
☐
2 marks

☐
Total for
this page

d) John measures the height of one of his healthy plants.

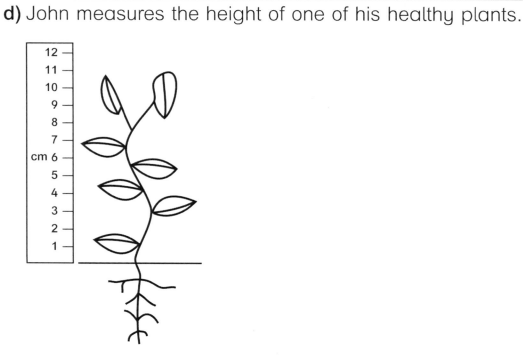

i) Tick the measurement that is right.

11 cm ☐   7 cm ☐   10 cm ☐

A/WS

☐

1 mark

ii) What else could he measure or count?

....

....

A/WS

☐

1 mark

/10

Total for this test

Name: _____ Class: _____ Date: _____

1. Give **two** ways in which these seeds are different from each other.

_____

_____

KU/WS

☐

2 marks

2. Class 2 is investigating what cress seeds need to start growing.

a) Group 1 wants to find out if seeds need water.
   They put some seeds in a dish with water.
   They put other seeds in a dish with no water.
   They put both dishes of seeds near the window.

	With water	No water
After two days		
After four days		

Draw what the seeds look like after two days with no water.

A

☐

1 mark

☐

Total for this page

b) Group 2 wants to find out if seeds need light to start to grow.

They put some seeds in a dish with water and put it near the window.

They put other seeds in a dish with water and put it in the cupboard.

After four days, they looked at the seeds.

i) Did the seeds near the window grow?

yes ☐   no ☐

KU

☐

1 mark

ii) Did the seeds in the cupboard grow?

yes ☐   no ☐

KU

☐

1 mark

c) Daniel said that Group 2 should not have given the seeds in the cupboard any water.

i) Is he right?

yes ☐   no ☐

A/WS

☐

1 mark

ii) Explain why.

....

....

A/WS

☐

1 mark

☐

Total for
this page

25

3. Ali bought his mum some bulbs for her birthday.

    The instructions say:

    • Plant the bulbs in a pot.
    • Water the bulbs.
    • Put the bulbs in a warm cupboard for a week.

    Mum thinks bulbs need to be in the light. They will not start to grow in the cupboard.

    a) Is she right?

    yes ☐   no ☐

    A
    ☐
    1 mark

    b) Explain why.

    _____

    _____

    A
    ☐
    1 mark

4. What does a seed need so that it can start to grow?

    _____

    KU
    ☐
    1 mark

/10

Total for this test

26

Name: _____ Class: _____ Date: _____

1. Class 2 wanted to find out about what plants need to keep healthy.

   They had four healthy plants to start with.

   After two weeks they recorded what had happened.

Plant	What it was given	Number of leaves	Colour of leaves	Height
A	☀️ 💧	8	green	10 cm
B	❌☀️ ❌💧		yellow	
C	❌☀️ 💧	4	yellow	17 cm
D		10	green	11 cm

a) Plant B had 4 leaves and measured 5 cm.
   Put this information in the table.

b) What was Plant D given?
   Write what it was given in the table.

c) What do all plants need to be healthy?

   _____

A/WS
☐
1 mark

A/WS
☐
1 mark

A
☐
1 mark

☐
Total for
this page

2. a) Put these pictures in order by joining them to the numbers.

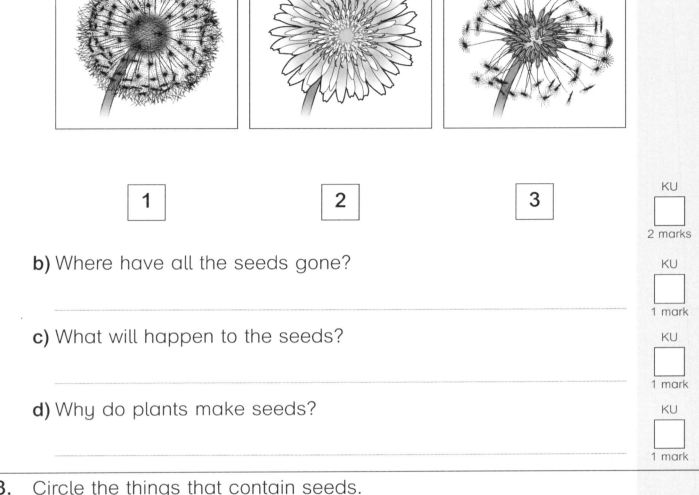

1	2	3

KU
☐
2 marks

b) Where have all the seeds gone?

....

KU
☐
1 mark

c) What will happen to the seeds?

....

KU
☐
1 mark

d) Why do plants make seeds?

....

KU
☐
1 mark

3.   Circle the things that contain seeds.

peanuts   cherries   sycamore   acorns

A/WS
☐
2 marks

/10

**Total for
this test**

Year 2
Animals, including humans
Test 1 (diagnostic assessment)

	Question	Answer	Extra information
1.	What do animals that live on land need to stay alive?	Air, food, water (shelter, right temperature)	
2.	Why does this animal live in a hole?	It is warm; safe; protected from other animals that might eat it; a good place to have its babies	*Use picture on page 30.*
3.	What do humans need to stay healthy?	Healthy diet, exercise, sleep	Some pupils may refer to keeping clean.
4.	Can you tell me the name of these groups of food?	Vegetables, dairy products	*Use pictures on page 31.*
5.	How could you find out what fruit the class eats most of?	Ask each child which fruit he/she eats most of; draw a graph; do a tally chart; keep a record; look in lunch boxes	
6.	Why should you wash your hands before you eat?	So you do not get dirt/germs inside you; so you do not get ill	Answers such as 'to keep healthy' and 'to make them clean' will need further questioning to elicit understanding.
7.	A foal is a young horse. Can you name a different young animal and say what it grows into?	Any young animal and its parent, e.g. calf and cow; puppy and dog; tadpole and frog	Some pupils will refer to the young as being, e.g. 'baby cat' and will need to be questioned further to elicit whether they know the correct name.

Animals, including humans
Test 1 (diagnostic assessment): pupil responses form

Q	Some pupils	Most pupils	All pupils
1.			
2.			
3.			
4.			
5.			
6.			
7.			

Animals, including humans
Test 1 (diagnostic assessment): question 2, visual prompt

Year 2
Animals, including humans
Test 1 (diagnostic assessment): question 4, visual prompts

Name: _____ Class: _____ Date: _____

1. Some children were talking about what animals that live on land need to survive.

   Circle the name of the child who is right.

   They need water, food and a home.

   Pat

   They need water, air and a home.

   Sam

   They need water, food and air.

   Sian

   KU

   1 mark

2. a) Every year, on his birthday, Mum measures Sami to see how much he has grown.

   Today is his 7th birthday.

   How tall is he?

   A/WS

   1 mark

   Total for this page

b) Mum writes down how tall he is and how much he has grown. Fill in the boxes for Sami's height and how much he has grown.

Age	Height	How much grown since last birthday
2 years	90 cm	
3 years	98 cm	8 cm
4 years	104 cm	6 cm
5 years	110 cm	6 cm
6 years	120 cm	10 cm
7 years		

A/WS
☐
2 marks

c) Tick the age that shows when Sami had grown most.

A/WS
☐
1 mark

3 ☐   4 ☐   5 ☐   6 ☐   7 ☐

d) Why might Mum have found it hard to measure Sami on his first birthday?

....

....

A
☐
1 mark

3. **a)** Sort the food into two groups. Draw arrows.

yoghurt   bread   butter   milk   potatoes   pasta

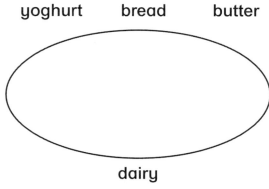

dairy   carbohydrates

KU
☐
2 marks

b) Write the name of one more food in **each** group.

KU
☐
2 marks

/10

Total for this test

Name: _____ Class: _____ Date: _____

1.

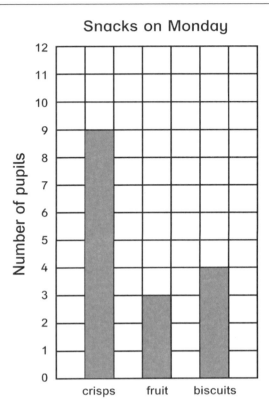

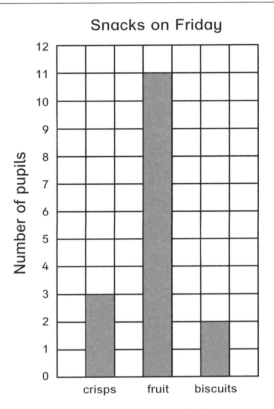

a) Class 2 made a bar chart of the snacks they ate on Monday.
Which snack did the fewest pupils eat?

1 mark

b) That week Class 2 learned about different foods the body needs.
They made a graph of the snacks they ate on Friday.
How many ate fruit on Friday?

1 mark

c) How many children are there in the class altogether?
Tick the right answer.

14 ☐   16 ☐   17 ☐   20 ☐

1 mark

Total for
this page

d) Look at the graph for snacks on Friday. Do you think the children had learned about foods that keep them healthy?

yes ☐   no ☐

How do you know?

....

A/WS
☐
1 mark

e) Why is fruit a healthy food?

....

KU
☐
1 mark

f) i) Write **one** reason why you should not eat too many biscuits.

....

KU
☐
1 mark

ii) Write **one** reason why you should not eat too many crisps.

....

KU
☐
1 mark

2.   a) Sort the food into **two** groups. Draw arrows.

pineapple   apple   yoghurt   grapes   cheese

A
☐
1 mark

b) Choose the right name and write it under each group.

| vegetables | dairy products | fruit | starchy foods |

KU
☐
2 marks

/10

Total for this test

Animals, including humans Test 4 (end of year)

Name: _____ Class: _____ Date: _____

1. Carla has a pet rabbit.
   Tick **three** things she **must** do
   to look after her rabbit.

   ☐ feed it every day   ☐ keep the cage clean

   ☐ make sure it always has water   ☐ talk to it

   ☐ give it water once a week   ☐ stroke it

   A/WS
   ☐
   2 marks

2. **a)** Match the animals to their young by drawing lines.

   KU
   ☐
   2 marks

   KU
   ☐
   2 marks

   ....

   b) Write the name of each young animal under its picture.

   ☐
   Total for
   this page

3. Write **one** reason why you should eat a balanced diet to keep you healthy.

KU

1 mark

....

4. a) Class 2 make a tally chart of the sports they like to do best. Complete the chart.

Sport	Tally	Number
running	ЖІ	5
swimming	ЖІ ІІІ	
football		12
tennis	ІІ	
cricket		3

b) Write the name of a different sport that would keep you healthy.

....

A/WS

2 marks

A

1 mark

/10

Total for this test

Year 2
Uses of everyday materials
Test 1 (diagnostic assessment)

	Question	Answer	Extra information
1.	When we talk about the material something is made from, what do we mean by the word 'material'?	An indication of an understanding that it is referring to the 'stuff' that it is made from, e.g. what it is made from; the stuff that is used to make it	Be aware of the common usage of the word to describe fabric.
2.	Can you tell me what this saucepan is made from? Why is this a good material for it to be made from?	Metal; aluminium; steel; stainless steel Any physical property which makes it suitable for cooking, e.g. it carries heat/lets the heat through; it can be used on the cooker without melting; it is waterproof	*Use a real object or picture (see page 39).*
3.	Can you tell me the name of something made from metal?	Any different object made from metal, e.g. coin; spoon; drinks can; nail	
4.	What will happen to this ball when you squash it?	It will change shape; it will go flat; it will go thin; it will go wide	*Use a real object or picture (see page 40).*
5.	What will happen to this t-shirt if you pull it at the top and the bottom?	It will change shape; it will get longer; it will stretch	*Use a real object or picture (see page 41), indicating where it is being pulled.*

Uses of everyday materials
Test 1 (diagnostic assessment): pupil responses form

Q	Some pupils	Most pupils	All pupils
1.			
2.			
3.			
4.			
5.			

Year 2
Uses of everyday materials
Test 1 (diagnostic assessment): question 2, visual prompt

Year 2
Uses of everyday materials
Test 1 (diagnostic assessment): question 4, visual prompt

Year 2
Uses of everyday materials
Test 1 (diagnostic assessment): question 5, visual prompt

Name: _____ Class: _____ Date: _____

1. a) Here is a shed.

   i) Circle **two** good materials to use for windows.

   plastic   **wood**   **metal**   **glass**

   KU ☐ 1 mark

   ii) Write **one** reason why these are good materials to use for windows.

   _____

   KU ☐ 1 mark

   b) i) Circle **two** good materials to use for walls.

   bricks   **wood**   **metal**   **glass**

   KU ☐ 1 mark

   ii) Write **one** reason why these are good materials to use for walls.

   _____

   KU ☐ 1 mark

☐ Total for this page

2. **a)** Class 2 found out about how objects can be made from different materials.

The table shows what they found out.

Object	Material			
	metal	plastic	glass	wood
spoon	✓	✓		✓
lunch box		✓		
ruler				

Put ticks in the table to show what materials a ruler can be made from.

b)  Lunch boxes can be made from other materials.

i) Circle the other materials that could be used to make a lunch box.

metal   **glass**   **wood**

ii) Explain why.

....

3. A ball can be made from foam.

a) Write **one** reason why foam is a good material for a ball.

....

b) Write **one** way that you can change the shape of a foam ball.

....

Name: _____ Class: _____ Date: _____

1. **a)** Class 2 are making 3D shapes out of plasticine.
Mia makes a cylinder.

| 1 2 3 4 5 6 7 8 9 10 11 12 |
| centimetres |

How long is it?

| A/WS |
| 1 mark |

b) Mia changes its shape.

| 1 2 3 4 5 6 7 8 9 10 11 12 |
| centimetres |

i) How long is it now?

| A/WS |
| 1 mark |

ii) Explain **one** way that she has changed it.

_____

| A |
| 1 mark |

c) Mia has **not** changed the amount of plasticine.
What has she done to change its shape?

_____

| KU |
| 1 mark |

| |
| Total for this page |

d) Tick the **two** sentences that are **true**.

☐ The narrower the cylinder is, the shorter it is.

☐ The wider the cylinder is, the longer it is.

☐ The wider the cylinder is, the shorter it is.

☐ The narrower the cylinder is, the longer it is.

A/WS
☐
2 marks

2. **a)** The class are making some fruit drinks.
They will need some cups for the drinks.

Cups are made from different materials.
Tick **two** materials that would be best for the children's cups.

plastic ☐   glass ☐   china ☐   cardboard ☐

KU
☐
2 marks

b) Explain why these are good materials for children's cups.

_____

KU
☐
1 mark

c) Cups can be made from different materials.
What must be the same about all cups?

All cups must be _____

_____

KU
☐
1 mark

/10

Total for this test

Year 2
Uses of everyday materials Test 4 (end of year)

Name: _____ Class: _____ Date: _____

1. a) Class 2 are doing a project called 'Houses around the World'.

How can they find information about houses from different parts of the world?

_____

A/WS

☐ 1 mark

b) The children found out that in different countries, the walls of houses are made from different materials.
Name **two** materials that are sometimes used for the walls of a house.

_____

_____

KU

☐ 2 marks

c) Circle **two** materials that are sometimes used for a roof.

slate   straw   bricks   cardboard

KU

☐ 1 mark

d) What does the roof material need to be? Tick **one**.

light ☐   waterproof ☐   bendy ☐

A

☐ 1 mark

☐ Total for this page

2. **a)** Tom has a rubber band that is 2 cm long. He adds different weights to the band and measures the length of the band.

The picture shows Tom's band with a 100 g weight. How long is Tom's band now?

Put your answer in the table.

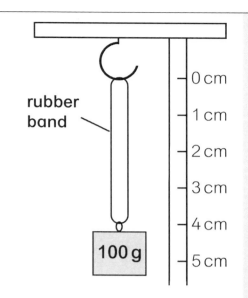

rubber band

Weight	Length of band
0 g	2 cm
100 g	
200 g	6 cm
300 g	8 cm

A/WS

1 mark

b) Tom made a bar chart of his results.

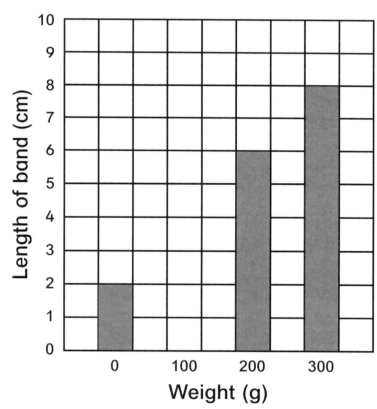

On the graph, draw the bar for 100 g.

A/WS

1 mark

Total for this page

c) Did the rubber band stretch by the same amount every time Tom added a weight?

yes □   **no** □

A/WS
□
1 mark

d) What happened to the rubber band when Tom took all the weights off?

Tick the correct statement.

□ It stayed the same length.

□ It broke.

□ It went back to the length it was to start with.

KU
□
1 mark

e) What would happen if Tom added too many weights?

KU
□
1 mark

/10

Total for this test

Answers and mark schemes

Year 2 Living things and their habitats*

* Accept phonically plausible spellings for all answers.

Test 2 (mid-topic)	Area	Mark	Extra information
1a. Living things or things that have been alive: dog, log, baby, tree non-living things: car, computer	KU/WS	2	All correct 2 marks Four or five correct 1 mark
1b. One suitable thing named	A	1	Accept any object made of wood, e.g. pencil
1c. One suitable thing named	A	1	
2. **Three** closely related to the following: move, eat, reproduce, grow, use their senses	KU	3	1 mark for each correct answer Accept drink **instead** of eat Accept breathe Accept excrete (or related) Do not accept walk or swim
3a. Where found: any suitable habitat, e.g. garden, flower bed, under stone	A/WS	2	1 mark for three or four names correct 1 mark for three or four habitats correct Accept in air as habitat for bee Accept wasp instead of bee
3b. A special place where plants or animals live and can find food and/or shelter	A	1	Accept an answer that shows an understanding that a habitat provides food and/or shelter

Living things and their habitats (continued)

Test 3 (end of topic)	Area	Mark	Extra information
1a. In a pond	A/WS	1	
1b. Caterpillars	A/WS	1	
1c. There is plenty for them to eat.	KU	1	Accept any reasonable answer relating to a flower bed being a suitable habitat
1d. Any **one** from: they cannot live in water or they would drown as they need air; butterflies cannot lay their eggs in water; they would not find the leaves they eat; they cannot swim.	KU	1	Accept any reasonable answer that relates to moving, eating or reproducing Accept that a pond is not the right habitat
2a. slug, woodlouse	KU	2	1 mark for each correct answer
2b. Any **one** from: it is warm; it is damp; it is dark; it provides protection; they can find food there	A	1	Accept any reasonable answer
2c. <table><thead><tr><th>Animal</th><th>Tally</th><th>Number</th></tr></thead><tbody><tr><td>worm</td><td>卌</td><td>5</td></tr><tr><td>snail</td><td>卌 ||||</td><td>9</td></tr><tr><td>slug</td><td>||||</td><td>4</td></tr><tr><td>spider</td><td>|||</td><td>3</td></tr><tr><td>beetle</td><td>卌 卌 |</td><td>11</td></tr></tbody></table>	A/WS	2	Tally marks for slug and beetle both correct for 1 mark Numbers for snail and spider both correct for 1 mark
3. Any animal that only eats meat	KU	1	Do not accept the name of an animal which is an omnivore (eats meat and plants), e.g. human Accept cat

Test 4 (end of year)	Area	Mark	Extra information
1. Cow; caterpillar; snail	KU	1	Two or three correct for 1 mark
2a. i) man	KU	1	
2a. ii) any suitable animals chosen to make a simple food chain	KU	2	1 mark for each box filled appropriately
2b. Give them one of each leaf at the same time	A/WS	1	
2c. Any answer that indicates that this will enable the snails to make a choice	A/WS	1	
2d. i) lettuce	A/WS	1	
2d. ii) dandelion	A/WS	1	
2e. yes	A	1	
2f. Any reasonable answer that refers to their habitat, e.g. that is where they live; they might not find anything to eat in a different place; they might get eaten	KU	1	Do not accept 'they might die' without a reason being given

Plants

Test 2 (mid-topic)	Area	Mark	Extra information
1. Give it water	KU	1	
2a. Shoots/leaves appear	KU	1	
2b. spring	A	1	
2c. More leaves appear; the leaves get longer; flowers appear	KU	1	Accept any one answer for 1 mark
3a. Bar at height of 5	A/WS	1	Only accept minimal tolerance of height
3b. Min	A/WS	1	
3c. light water soil	KU	2	Three correct 2 marks Two correct 1 mark
3d. i) 11 cm	A/WS	1	
3d. ii) The number of leaves; how big the leaves are	A/WS	1	Accept any one answer for 1 mark

Test 3 (end of topic)	Area	Mark	Extra information
1. Suitable references to difference in physical properties, e.g. size or shape; they will grow into different plants	KU/WS	2	Answers need to imply a comparison Accept two answers that both refer to physical differences 1 mark for each difference
2a. Drawing of seed similar to that drawn after four days with no water	A	1	
2b. i) yes	KU	1	
2b. ii) yes	KU	1	
2c. i) no	A/WS	1	
2c. ii) It would not have been a fair test or an indication that two different variables would have been used, i.e. water and light.	A/WS	1	
3a. no	A	1	
3b. Indication that seeds and bulbs do not need light to start growing	A	1	
4. Water (and warmth)	KU	1	

Plants (continued)

Test 4 (end of year)	Area	Mark	Extra information
1a. 4 and 5 cm written in correct boxes in Plant B row	A/WS	1	Both correct for 1 mark
1b. Light **and** water	A/WS	1	
1c. Light **and** water	A	1	
2a. 1 flower 2 complete seed head 3 seed head with most seeds gone	KU	2	All correct for 2 marks One correct for 1 mark
2b. They have been blown away.	KU	1	Accept that they have gone away from the plant
2c. Accept any answer that implies that they will grow into new plants.	KU	1	Accept that they might get eaten
2d. To reproduce or make new plants	KU	1	
3. All four circled	A/WS	2	All correct for 2 marks Three correct for 1 mark Accept one circle around all drawings for 2 marks

Animals, including humans

Test 2 (mid-topic)	Area	Mark	Extra information
1. Sian	KU	1	
2a. 125 cm	A/WS	1	
2b. 125 cm in bottom box of 'height' column 5 cm in bottom box of 'how much grown' column	A/WS	2	1 mark for each column filled in correctly Accept number only
2c. 6	A/WS	1	
2d. He could not stand up; he would not keep still.	A	1	Accept any sensible reason why it could have been difficult to measure the baby
3a. Dairy: yoghurt, butter and milk Carbohydrates: bread, potatoes and pasta	KU	2	1 mark for each group defined correctly
3b. A suitable food added to **each** group, e.g. cheese to dairy products, rice to carbohydrates	KU	2	1 mark for each suitable food

Test 3 (end of topic)	Area	Mark	Extra information
1a. Fruit	A/WS	1	
1b. 11	A/WS	1	
1c. 16	A/WS	1	
1d. yes – more pupils ate fruit or no – some pupils still ate biscuits and crisps	A/WS	1	
1e. It contains vitamins; it contains minerals; it gives you energy; it does not make you fat.	KU	1	Accept any one answer for 1 mark Do not accept 'it makes you healthy'
1f. i) Biscuits contain a lot of sugar; they can damage your teeth; they can make you fat.	KU	1	Accept any one answer for 1 mark
1f. ii) Crisps contain a lot of salt; they contain a lot of fat; they can make you fat.	KU	1	Accept any one answer for 1 mark
2a. pineapple, apple, grapes and yoghurt, cheese	A	1	
2b. fruit dairy products	KU	2	1 mark for each group labelled correctly

Animals, including humans (continued)

Test 4 (end of year)	Area	Mark	Extra information
1. feed it every day make sure it always has water keep the cage clean	A/WS	2	All three correct 2 marks Two correct 1 mark
2a. tadpole to frog chick to hen kitten to cat caterpillar to butterfly	KU	2	All correct 2 marks Two correct 1 mark
2b. Correct name written under each young animal	KU	2	All correct 2 marks Two or three correct 1 mark Accept phonically plausible spellings.
3. To give you energy; to help you grow (may make specific reference to bones); to help you get better if you are ill; to help look after your teeth	KU	1	Accept any reasonable answer that is related
4a. <table><tr><td>Sport</td><td>Tally</td><td>Number</td></tr><tr><td>running</td><td>‖‖</td><td>5</td></tr><tr><td>swimming</td><td>‖‖ ‖‖</td><td>8</td></tr><tr><td>football</td><td>‖‖ ‖‖ ‖‖</td><td>12</td></tr><tr><td>tennis</td><td>‖‖</td><td>2</td></tr><tr><td>cricket</td><td>‖‖‖</td><td>3</td></tr></table>	A/WS	2	Tally marks for football and cricket both correct 1 mark Numbers for swimming and tennis both correct 1 mark
4b. Name of any active sport, e.g. basketball, cycling, skipping, dance, rugby	A	1	

Uses of everyday materials

Test 2 (mid-topic)	Area	Mark	Extra information
1a. i) plastic, glass	KU	1	Both correct for 1 mark
1a. ii) They are both transparent; they let the light through; you can see through them.	KU	1	Accept any one answer for 1 mark
1b. i) wood, bricks	KU	1	Both correct for 1 mark
1b. ii) They are rigid; they do not bend	KU	1	Accept any one answer for 1 mark Accept they are tough or strong
2a. Metal, plastic, wood	A/WS	1	Two or three correct for 1 mark
2b. i) metal, wood	A/WS	2	1 mark for each correct material
2b. ii) Any reference made to suitable physical properties, e.g. rigidity; strength; waterproofness	A/WS	1	Accept the food would not get squashed
3a. It is light; it won't hurt if it hits you; you can kick/throw it a long way; you can wash it if it gets dirty; it is cheap	KU	1	Accept any one answer for 1 mark
3b. Squash it; push it; pull it; twist it; put something heavy on it	A	1	Accept any one answer for 1 mark

Test 3 (end of topic)	Area	Mark	Extra information
1a. 10 cm	A/WS	1	Accept an answer between 9.5 and 10.5 cm Unit required
1b. i) 6 cm	A/WS	1	Accept an answer between 5.5 and 6.5 cm Unit required
1b. ii) It is shorter; it is wider or fatter	A	1	Accept any one answer that clearly indicates that the length or width has changed for 1 mark Do not accept that it is smaller
1c. Squashed it; pressed down on it; put a weight on it	KU	1	Accept any reasonable answer that indicates that a force has been used
1d. The wider the cylinder is, the shorter it is The narrower the cylinder is, the longer it is	A/WS	2	1 mark for each correct sentence
2a. plastic, cardboard	KU	2	1 mark for each correct material
2b. They do not break.	KU	1	Accept any answer that refers to them being inexpensive
2c. Waterproof/do not let the drink go through	KU	1	

Uses of everyday materials (continued)

Test 4 (end of year)	Area	Mark	Extra information
1a. Use the Internet; look it up in a book; ask someone who has been to a different country	A/WS	1	Accept any one answer for 1 mark Allow research
1b. Any **two** from: stone; brick; wood; bamboo; felt; canvas; metal	KU	2	Accept any other suitable materials
1c. slate, straw	KU	1	Both correct for 1 mark
1d. Waterproof	A	1	
2a. 4 cm added to table	A/WS	1	
2b. Bar for 100 g drawn to 4	A/WS	1	Minimal tolerance for height, ignore width
2c. yes	A/WS	1	
2d. It went back to the length it was to start with.	KU	1	
2e. It would break/snap.	KU	1	